King Alfred's
Winchester

Adventure in Rio

ELEMENTARY LEVEL

Series Editor: John Milne

The Heinemann ELT Guided Readers provide a choice of enjoyable reading material for learners of English. The series is published at five levels – Starter, Beginner, Elementary, Intermediate and Upper. At **Elementary Level**, the control of content and language has the following main features:

Information Control

Stories have straightforward plots and a restricted number of main characters. Information which is vital to the understanding of the story is clearly presented and repeated when necessary. Difficult allusion and metaphor are avoided and cultural backgrounds are made explicit.

Structure Control

Students will meet those grammatical features which they have already been taught in their elementary course of studies. Other grammatical features occasionally occur with which the students may not be so familiar, but their use is made clear through context and reinforcement. This ensures that the reading as well as being enjoyable provides a continual learning situation for the students. Sentences are kept short – a maximum of two clauses in nearly all cases – and within sentences there is a balanced use of simple adverbial and adjectival phrases. Great care is taken with pronoun reference.

Vocabulary Control

At **Elementary Level** there is a limited use of a carefully controlled vocabulary of approximately 1,100 basic words. At the same time, students are given some opportunity to meet new or unfamiliar words in contexts where their meaning is obvious. The meaning of words introduced in this way is reinforced by repetition. Help is also given to the students in the form of vivid illustrations which are very closely related to the text.

Contents

Note

This story takes place in England and Brazil, in the 1970s. There were not many fax machines then, and people could not send and receive e-mails. This story is about scientists and inventors. But at that time, everybody had to use the telephones and the postal services when they wanted to talk to each other, or send each other information.

1

The Man With Cruel Eyes

Neil Garton was a good-looking young man. He was twenty-two years old and he was an engineer. He worked for an inventor called Russell Bowden. Neil was Russell Bowden's assistant.

Russell Bowden was fifty years old. He had long white hair and he wore thick glasses. Russell was an inventor – he made things which nobody had made before. Neil liked working for Russell. His job was exciting.

Russell Bowden's workshop was in Brighton – a large town in Sussex, on the south coast of England. Neil Garton had been a student in the town. He had studied engineering at Brighton College of Technology. When Neil finished his studies, Russell had given him the job.

For many years, Russell Bowden had been working on a secret project. He wanted to make a different kind of car – an electric car. He wanted to make a car which did not use petrol!

Many other people had made electric cars, but they had not been successful. The problem with these electric cars was in the batteries.

Electricity had to be stored in batteries, and batteries did not last for ever! Some electric cars had been built, but their drivers had to recharge the batteries very often. They could not go on long journeys.

Russell Bowden wanted to make a new kind of battery. He wanted to build a car which could travel one thousand miles before the batteries had to be recharged.

Neil Garton worked for an inventor called Russell Bowden.

Russell had been working on this problem for a long time. And now he was worried. The battery project was a very expensive one. Russell had already spent a lot of money on the project. Now, he needed some more money. He needed to borrow money from a bank.

Neil Garton was worried too.

'If Russell cannot get more money from a bank, he will have to close his business,' Neil thought. 'Then I will lose my job.'

Russell Bowden had many enemies. Anyone who tried to make a new kind of electric car had enemies. Russell wanted to make his electric car very much. But his enemies wanted to sell oil!

There were many people in the world who were very rich because oil was very expensive. But there was something which frightened them! If an inventor made a successful electric car, petrol would become very cheap. And petrol was made from oil. So if an inventor made a successful electric car, oil would become cheap too. Then these rich people's lives would change. People who owned oil wells, people who owned oil-refineries, people who owned garages – all those rich people would lose money!

One of these people was Dr Lurcher. Dr Lurcher was a very rich man. He was one of the richest men in the world. He owned companies in every country in the world. He owned oil wells in North America. He owned oil-refineries in South America. And he owned garages in Europe.

Dr Lurcher was a very secretive man. No one knew everything about Dr Lurcher's companies.

Dr Lurcher had many passports. But there was a different name on each passport. And the photograph in each passport had a different face. In one passport, Dr Lurcher was an old man with a beard. In another passport, he was a young man with a small moustache.

Dr Lurcher was a cruel and ruthless man. If anyone tried to work against him, he always stopped them. And, of course, Dr Lurcher always tried to stop anyone making a successful electric car.

Dr Lurcher had spies in every country in the world. These spies found out what scientists and engineers were doing. They found out what inventors were making. And these spies sent reports to Dr Lurcher.

_____

One day, one of Lurcher's spies in Britain heard about a man called Russell Bowden. The spy visited Brighton. He asked many people about Russell Bowden. And he soon found out everything about Russell. Russell Bowden was an inventor, and he was trying to make a new kind of battery for an electric car. The spy was very interested in this news!

The spy wrote a report and sent it to Dr Lurcher. Dr Lurcher read the report. He was very interested too. Dr Lurcher decided to visit Russell Bowden in his small workshop near Brighton.

_____

One Friday afternoon, a huge black car drove up to Russell Bowden's workshop. Neil Garton was alone in the workshop because Russell had gone to London.

When Neil heard the noise of a car, he opened the door. Neil saw two tough men get out of the car. One man was tall and thin with short, black hair. The other was a small, fat man. He was wearing a panama hat.

Neil went outside to talk to them. The tall, thin man was speaking to someone in the car.

'This is the place, sir,' he said.

Then a third man got out of the car. This man had a small pointed beard and cold, cruel eyes.

'Are you Bowden?' the bearded man asked rudely.

'I'm sorry,' said Neil politely. 'Mr Bowden isn't here today. My name is Neil Garton. Can I help you?'

'I'm Dr Lurcher,' the man said. 'These are my friends, Frank and Pete.'

Frank was the tall, thin man with short, black hair. Pete was the small, fat man with the panama hat. They both looked cruel and unfriendly.

Frank spoke quietly to Dr Lurcher.

'It's strange, sir,' he said. 'Someone called Garton is making trouble for us in Rio de Janeiro. And now, here's someone called Garton in Brighton. Is *this* Garton going to make trouble for us too?'

'We don't have to worry about this man,' said Dr Lurcher. 'He's easy to deal with. He works for Bowden, and Bowden isn't a rich man. Bowden is trying to borrow money. And we can stop the banks lending him money. We can stop Bowden's project!'

'But Garton in Rio is going to give us much more trouble,' went on Dr Lurcher. 'He is a very rich man. It won't be easy to stop his project.'

Neil heard what the men were saying. But he did not understand what they were talking about.

'Bowden isn't here – what a pity!' said Dr Lurcher to Neil. 'But you can give Bowden a message from me. He's planning to make an electric car. Tell him, "Dr Lurcher doesn't want anyone to make an electric car." Give him that message!'

Neil became angry. Who was this Dr Lurcher?

'What is your business with Mr Bow—?' Neil began to ask. But he was not able to finish. Dr Lurcher said something which surprised him.

'Bowden will not be able to borrow money from any bank in London,' he said. 'A man who wants to make electric cars is a madman. And banks do not lend money to madmen.'

'Russell *is* trying to borrow money,' Neil thought. 'But how does this man Lurcher know that?'

Lurcher got back into his car. The small, fat man started to close the door. But before the door closed, Lurcher spoke again.

'Tell Bowden to invent something else!' he said to Neil. 'Tell him to invent an electric rocket which will take him to the moon!'

The two men with Dr Lurcher laughed loudly. Then they got into the car and drove away.

Russell Bowden Gets a Present

Later that same Friday afternoon, another visitor arrived at the workshop. It was a courier on a motorbike.

The courier was wearing a black leather jacket and black leather trousers. Neil Garton could not see the courier's face because it was hidden under a large black crash helmet.

The courier gave a package to Neil.

'What's this?' asked Neil.

'It's not my job to know what things are,' said the messenger rudely. 'I'm a messenger. It's my job to deliver things to an address. Look! It's written on the package – Russell Bowden, Unit 15. This is Unit 15. I can see that!'

Neil took the package from the courier, who drove away quickly.

Neil put the package on Russell's untidy desk in their office. He was unhappy about the package. But he did not know why.

'There's something strange about this package,' he thought.

Russell Bowden got back from London late in the afternoon. A taxi brought him from the station.

When Russell got out of the taxi, he did not look happy. He stood outside Unit 15. Something was wrong! Neil went outside to speak to him.

'I've got bad news,' Russell told Neil. 'I've been to my bank in London. But the manager has refused to lend me any more money. I don't know why. We won't be able to go on working much longer. If I can't borrow money, I can't pay you.'

'I know why you can't borrow any money,' said Neil. And he told Russell about the visit from Dr Lurcher and the two other men.

'Now I understand,' said Russell. 'I've heard about Lurcher. He's a very rich man. And he's a very powerful and ruthless man. He doesn't want anyone to make a successful electric car. He'll do anything to stop them. Now he's told lies about me to the banks. He has said, "Bowden is a madman." He's told the banks not to lend me any money.'

'A courier on a motorbike brought a package, this afternoon,' said Neil. 'He came after Lurcher's visit. The package is for you. I've put it on your desk.'

'Who sent it?' asked Russell. '

'I don't know,' replied Neil.

'Let's look at it,' said Russell.

The two men went into the office. But as soon as he saw the package, Russell stopped. He put out his arm and stopped Neil.

'Shhh! There's something wrong,' he said quietly. 'Don't move. Listen!'

They both stood still and listened. There was a noise coming from the package. It was the ticking of a clock.

'Shhh! There's something wrong,' Russell said quietly.

'It must be a present from Dr Lurcher,' said Russell after a moment. 'Let's see what's inside it!'

'No!' said Neil excitedly. 'Perhaps it's a bomb! You mustn't touch it. I'll call the police.'

'No, no! Don't do that!' said Russell. 'If we call the police, everybody will read about our problems in the newspapers. That will give people another reason for not lending me any money.'

'What are we going to do?' asked Neil.

'Don't worry,' said Russell. 'I know what to do.'

Russell opened the parcel. There was a clock inside it, and the clock was ticking loudly. Then suddenly, it stopped ticking.

Neil shouted a warning to Russell.

'Get down, Russell!' he shouted. Then he threw himself onto the floor.

Russell laughed.

'It's all right, Neil,' he said. 'You can get up now. Look! There's only a clock and two batteries. The only other thing in the package is this note.

The two men read the note.

'I'm worried about these things that are happening,' Russell said to Neil. 'You'll be in danger if you go on working for me. Perhaps you should get another job, Neil.'

'Nonsense!' said Neil angrily. 'No one is going to frighten me! If you want me to stay and work for you, I'll stay.'

Then Neil remembered something about Lurcher and his friend, Frank. They had spoken about a man called Garton, in Rio de Janeiro.

'One of the men with Dr Lurcher said something that I didn't understand,' said Neil. 'When I told them my name, one of the men said it was strange.'

'What's strange about your name?' asked Russell.

'A man called Garton is making trouble for Lurcher in Brazil – in Rio de Janeiro,' said Neil. 'And I'm called Garton too. I was making trouble for them in Brighton. Lurcher said, "He's easy to deal with. He works for Bowden and Bowden isn't a rich man. But Garton in Rio is going to give us much more trouble." Do you know who this other Garton is, Russell?'

'Yes, I do. His name is Rufus Garton,' said Russell.

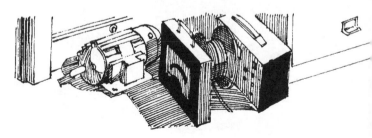

'Rufus – that's an unusual name,' said Neil. 'I had an uncle called Rufus. He went to live in Rio de Janeiro many years ago. Perhaps this man is my uncle.'

'Yes, perhaps he is,' said Russell. 'I've met Rufus Garton. I met him a few times in South America. He's an inventor, like me. He was trying to make cheaper electricity. We used to write to one another. I have his letters somewhere in my desk. Let's find his phone number. I must phone him and tell him about Lurcher.'

3

'My Phones Are Bugged!'

Russell quickly found the phone number of Rufus Garton's office on a letter. Then he looked in a phone book to find the dialling code for Rio de Janeiro.

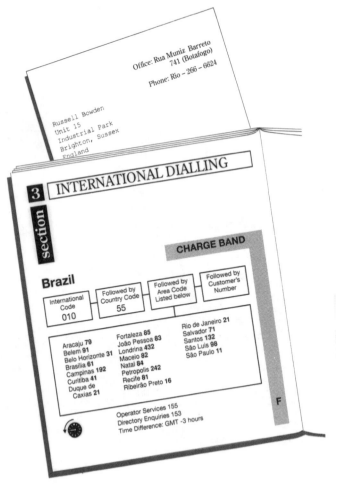

Office: Rua Muniz Barreto
741 (Botafogo)

Phone: Rio – 266 – 6624

Russell Bowden
Unit 15
Industrial Park
Brighton, Sussex
England

3 **INTERNATIONAL DIALLING**

section

CHARGE BAND

Brazil

International Code	Followed by Country Code	Followed by Area Code Listed below	Followed by Customer's Number
010	55		

Aracaju **79**	Fortaleza **85**	Rio de Janeiro **21**
Belem **91**	João Pessoa **83**	Salvador **71**
Belo Horizonte **31**	Londrina **432**	Santos **132**
Brasilia **61**	Maceio **82**	São Luis **98**
Campinas **192**	Natal **84**	São Paulo **11**
Curitiba **41**	Petropolis **242**	
Duque de	Recife **81**	
Caxias **21**	Ribeirão Preto **16**	

F

Operator Services 155
Directory Enquiries 153
Time Difference: GMT -3 hours

'What's the time now?' Russell asked Neil.

'It's 6.30 p.m.,' Neil replied. 'It's too late to phone Rio de Janeiro now. Rufus won't be in his office. He'll be at home.'

'No, he won't,' said Russell. 'Look at the dialling-code book again. Look at the line where it says GMT minus three hours. GMT is Greenwich Mean Time – the time here in the UK. Rio is three hours behind us. It's only 3.30 p.m. in Rio now.'

Russell rang Rufus Garton's phone number. He got no reply. He rang again and again but no one replied. Then Russell remembered something.

'It's winter here in the UK,' he said to Neil. 'But it's summer in Brazil. It's hot in Brazil in the afternoons. There, everyone sleeps in the afternoon. Let's go and have a meal now. We'll come back and phone Rufus Garton at nine o'clock. Then it will be six o'clock in Rio. I'm sure that Rufus Garton will be in his office at that time.'

Russell and Neil took a bus into the centre of Brighton and they went into an Indian restaurant to have a meal.

'How do you know so much about Rio?' Neil asked Russell.

'I've been to Brazil many times, Neil,' replied Russell. 'For many years, I've been interested in what the scientists there were doing. Brazilian scientists have had many wonderful ideas. One of them invented a car that runs on alcohol. You can make alcohol from sugar-cane. And sugar-cane is very easy to grow in Brazil. So in Brazil, you can run your car cheaply on alcohol.'

'You're only interested in cars!' said Neil, laughing.

'Well, what do *you* know about Brazil?' asked Russell.

'I know that the Brazilians are good at football,' Neil replied. 'They won the World Cup in 1958 and 1962 and 1970. And Rio de Janeiro is famous for its beautiful girls and its beautiful beaches!'

'Ah, young men only think about football and beautiful girls!' said Russell, smiling.

'Yes!' said Neil. 'Now, tell me more about Rufus Garton,'

'I haven't met him often,' said Russell. 'I've met him two or three times in Rio.'

'I've been thinking about his first name – Rufus,' Neil said. 'It's a very unusual name. I told you about my Uncle Rufus. He was my father's brother. He went to live in Rio de Janeiro many years ago. I wonder if this *is* the same man?'

'Strange things do happen,' said Russell.

'Well, my mother died when I was very young,' Neil explained. 'Soon after that, my father died too. I was an orphan. I have no brothers and sisters. I went to live in an orphanage. I lived there until I came to college in Brighton. I know very little about my uncle. But his name is Rufus and he does live in Brazil.'

'When I speak to Rufus Garton on the phone, I will ask him about you,' said Russell.

Back in the office, Russell picked up the phone on his desk. He was going to speak to Rufus Garton. Russell dialled Rufus Garton's number.

'Hello. Who is calling please?' a man said in Portuguese.

Russell answered in English.

'This is Russell Bowden in England,' he said. 'Can I speak to Rufus Garton, please?'

Suddenly, Russell heard a loud whistling noise. After a few seconds, the noise stopped.

'I am Rufus Garton,' the man said. He spoke in English now. 'This is very strange, Russell. I was going to call you this evening. But listen, I can't talk now. Put your phone down and wait for me to phone you. Don't go away. I want to speak to you urgently.'

'Wait a moment—' Russell began. But it was too late. Rufus Garton had put down his phone.

Russell and Neil sat in the office and waited. Ten minutes passed. Then twenty minutes. After half an hour, Neil became impatient.

'This is silly!' he said. 'He's not going to phone back. Let's go home!'

At that moment, the phone started to ring. Russell picked it up. There was another phone in the office. Neil picked up the other phone. He was going to listen to the conversation.

'Russell Bowden here,' Russell said.

'I've kept you waiting,' said Rufus Garton. 'I'm sorry. I had to drive to a friend's flat. That's where I'm phoning from now. Listen carefully.

'I'm phoning from my friend's flat,' Garton went on, 'because my own phones are bugged! I'm sure about that. Whenever I speak on the phone, someone else is listening. Someone has bugged my phones at home and in the office.

'And I'm being followed,' he continued. 'I'm followed everywhere that I go. If I go anywhere by car, someone follows me in a car. If I walk anywhere, someone follows me on foot.'

'I'm phoning you because my assistant was visited today by a man called Dr Lurcher,' said Russell. 'My assistant heard Lurcher and his men speaking about a man called Garton. This man, Garton, lives in Rio. That is why I'm phoning you – to warn you.'

'Dr Lurcher!' said Rufus. 'I know about that man. And I know what he wants!'

'What *does* he want?' asked Russell.

'My friend, do you remember my project?' said Rufus. 'I always wanted to send electric power from one place to another without wires. I wanted to send electricity through the air, guided by laser beams.'

'Yes, I remember your project,' said Russell. 'It isn't possible. I told you that a long time ago.'

'Well, you were wrong! It *is* possible,' said Rufus. 'At last, I've been successful. I've made a successful experiment. And I've made notes about it. Now Lurcher is trying to steal the notes. I'm sure of that!'

'Send your notes to me, Rufus,' said Russell. 'I'll keep them safe from Lurcher.'

'But Lurcher's men are watching you too,' replied Rufus. 'If I send anything to you, they might get it first.'

'What about me?' said Neil suddenly. He spoke into the other phone. 'Send the notes to me. Lurcher's men don't know my address.'

'Who are you?' asked Rufus Garton.

'This is my assistant,' Russell explained. 'His name is Garton – he has the same name as yours. Perhaps you are his uncle, Rufus. He had an uncle whose name was Rufus. But that uncle went to Brazil a long time ago.'

'How strange!' said Rufus. 'I've been trying to find my nephew for many years.'

'But that is not important at the moment,' said Russell. 'The important thing is getting your notes safely to us.'

'I agree,' said Rufus Garton. 'I'll put all my notes in a package and send them to your assistant. What's his address?'

Russell gave Neil's address in Brighton to Rufus.

'Good,' said Rufus. 'Today is Friday. I'll finish writing my notes over the weekend. I'll send them to Neil on Monday morning. I'll send them by special courier. My friend, Antonio Severo, will send the notes for me. I'm phoning from his flat now. Either Antonio or his daughter, Miriam, will send the notes for me.'

4

Kidnap in Rio

It was early afternoon on the Tuesday of the following week. The warm sun was shining down on the sands of Flamengo Beach in the beautiful city of Rio de Janeiro.

At the north end of Flamengo Beach is Gloria Bay. By the shore, there are beautiful gardens – gardens full of brightly coloured flowers. There is a large marina at Gloria Bay. Many people in Rio own boats. They keep them at the marina. And from the marina there is the view of a mountain, far across Guanabara Bay.

This mountain is Sugarloaf. Sugarloaf is four hundred metres high. Visitors travel to the top of the mountain by cable-car. The cable-car takes them first to the top of a smaller mountain, Morro da Urca, which is in front of Sugarloaf. Then the car goes on, up to the top of Sugarloaf itself.

On that Tuesday afternoon, the sun was shining brightly, and Sugarloaf stood against the clear blue sky. And something was happening at the marina. A luxury yacht was arriving.

The name of the yacht was the *Oil King*. It was bigger than any of the other yachts in the marina. Someone was sitting on the deck of the yacht. It was the owner of the boat. He was wearing shorts and he was enjoying the sunshine.

Two men were standing beside him. But they were not wearing shorts. They were wearing suits with jackets. The men looked hot and uncomfortable.

Frank and Pete were wearing jackets because they were carrying guns. The guns were hidden under their jackets. Dr Lurcher did not need a gun.

As soon as the *Oil King* arrived in the marina, a small, fast boat went out to meet it. Two young men climbed up onto the deck of the *Oil King*. The men looked tough. One of them had short dark hair and a small moustache. The other man had curly hair. He was clean-shaven and he had tattoos on his arms.

'Have you anything to report?' Lurcher asked the two men. 'What is Rufus Garton doing?'

'A man called Bowden phoned him from the UK last Friday, sir,' said the man with the tattoos. 'As soon as he got the call, Garton told Bowden to put his phone down. Then he went to the flat of his friend, Antonio Severo, the lawyer. Perhaps he phoned Bowden from there. We haven't been able to bug Severo's phone. So we don't know what he said.'

'What did Garton do after that?' asked Lurcher.

'He went back to his own flat and he stayed there all weekend,' said the man with the small moustache.

'And what has Garton done since the weekend?' asked Lurcher.

'Nothing. He has stayed at home,' the man replied.

'Did he have any visitors?' asked Lurcher.

'Yes,' said the tattooed man. 'Severo's daughter, Miriam, visited his flat. She's a young, tall girl with long dark hair. She's about twenty-one years old. She works with her father in his office. She visited Garton yesterday. She was carrying a large package. She stayed for an hour. Then she left with the same package.'

'*Was* it the same package?' asked Lurcher, quickly. 'How do you know that?'

There was silence for a few moments.

'We didn't think about that,' said the man with tattoos. 'It *looked* the same.'

Dr Lurcher laughed loudly.

'Garton is a clever man! He has tricked both of you,' he said.

Lurcher quickly gave orders to all his men. The man with the small moustache was called Pedro. Pedro was told to take Frank with him to Rufus Garton's flat.

'Pedro! said Lurcher. 'Show Frank where Garton lives. Help him if he needs any help.'

Frank laughed. 'I won't need any help!' he said.

The tattooed man was called Miguel. Miguel was told to take Pete with him to Severo's flat.

'Miguel! Show Pete where Severo lives,' said Lurcher.

'Severo will not be at home,' said Miguel. 'He is a busy lawyer. He will be at his office.'

'Good!' said Lurcher. 'Take Pete there. I want both Severo and his daughter.'

The four men got into the small boat.

'Bring me Garton, Severo and his daughter!' Lurcher shouted to them. 'Don't let them trick you again!'

The small boat started towards the city. Lurcher smiled and went back to his chair.

———

That Tuesday afternoon, Rufus Garton was sitting in his flat. His entry phone buzzed. Somebody was at the street door. Rufus spoke into the entryphone.

'Who's there?' he asked.

'I'm a messenger,' said the voice. 'I have something for you, Mr Garton.'

Rufus was puzzled. Who was it? Was it someone with a message from Russell Bowden? He pressed the button of the entryphone. It opened the main door to the block of flats. Rufus opened his flat door and waited.

The lift came up, but it did not stop at Rufus' floor. Was the messenger walking up the stairs? Rufus walked over to the stairway and looked down. Suddenly, he heard a voice behind him.

'Turn round very slowly,' the voice said.

Rufus turned and saw a man with a gun. Frank had stayed in the lift. The lift had gone up to the next floor. On the floor above, Frank had got out of the lift and quietly walked down the stairs. This was an old trick.

'Someone wants to talk to you,' said Frank. 'Come with me. And come quietly!'

Rufus looked at the man's face.

'Yes,' he thought. 'I'll go quietly with him.'

———

Antonio Severo was a busy lawyer. People often visited him in his office. So Antonio was not surprised when his secretary, Roberto, spoke to him on the internal phone. It was about four o'clock.

'There are two men to see you,' said Roberto. 'They won't give their names.'

'What do they want?' Antonio asked.

'They won't tell me,' said Roberto.

'OK. Send them in,' said the lawyer.

Roberto was surprised when Mr Severo left the office a few moments later. The two men were walking closely behind the lawyer. Where were they going?

When Miriam Severo arrived at the office later that afternoon, she was puzzled.

'Where's my father?' she asked Roberto.

'He went out with two men, about two hours ago,' Roberto told Miriam. 'He didn't say anything as he was leaving. It was very strange.'

Then the phone rang. Miriam picked it up.

'Miriam Severo?' a rough voice asked.

'Yes, that's me,' the girl replied.

'I've a message for you from your father,' said the man with the rough voice.

'Where is he?' asked Miriam. 'Why can't he speak to me himself?'

'Your father is visiting us,' the man said. 'He's come here with Mr Rufus Garton. And they want you to come here and join us.'

'Let me speak to my father,' said Miriam. 'I won't do anything unless I can speak to my father.'

'There's no phone near your father,' the man replied. 'He wants you to come and he wants you to bring something important with you.'

'What are you talking about?' Miriam asked.

'Rufus Garton gave you some papers yesterday,' said the man. 'Your father wants you to bring him those papers.'

'I don't understand you,' said Miriam. 'I don't know anything about any papers.'

Miriam heard two people talking at the other end of the phone line. Then the rough voice spoke again.

'I'll call you again tomorrow morning,' the man said. 'Wait for my call in your office.'

5

Prisoners on Lurcher's Island

There are many small islands in the large bay between Rio and the opposite shore at Niteroi. Some of these islands are owned by very, very rich people. The islands are very, very private.

On that same Tuesday evening, at seven o'clock, three men were sitting on the verandah of a large, luxurious villa. The villa was on one of the private islands. The villa, and the island, were owned by Dr Lurcher. He had moved his yacht from the marina to the island. And he was one of the men on the verandah. The other two men were Frank and Pete. Rufus Garton and Antonio Severo were prisoners in the cellars of this villa. They were locked in separate rooms.

'What shall we do now?' Pete asked Lurcher. 'Rufus Garton's project was a failure and he has burnt all the notes. That's what he says. Severo doesn't know anything about them. That's what *he* says. But Severo's daughter took a package out of Garton's flat yesterday. So where is the package now?'

'Let me deal with these people,' said Frank. 'I'll make them talk!'

'I've got a better idea,' said Lurcher. 'Bring Severo's daughter here. When Garton and Severo hear about it, they'll tell us everything!'

'It'll be easy to get her,' said Pete. 'I told her to wait for a phone call tomorrow morning. She is very worried about her father. She will be waiting by the phone in her father's office.'

*Three men were sitting on the verandah of
a large, luxurious villa*

'Good! You can go to the marina again in the morning,' Lurcher replied.

———

It was seven o'clock on Tuesday evening. Roberto had left the office and Miriam was alone there. She was sitting at her father's desk.

'What shall I do now?' she asked herself.

She had sent the package to Britain by courier. The package was addressed to someone called Neil Garton. And he was going to give it to the man called Russell Bowden.

'I must get the package back,' she said.

Rufus had Bowden's phone number in his flat. And there was a key to the flat in her father's desk drawer.

But was it safe to go to Rufus Garton's flat? Perhaps someone was watching it.

Suddenly, Miriam remembered the address on the package which she had sent to Britain – Neil Garton, 5 Brook Street, Brighton, Sussex, UK. Miriam quickly phoned International Enquiries and asked for Neil Garton's phone number.

Miriam checked the time on her watch. It was just after seven o'clock. It would be ten o'clock in the UK.

Miriam dialled Neil's number and she waited.

'Hello, this is Brighton 765432,' said a voice.

'Is that Neil Garton?' Miriam asked.

'Yes, this is Neil Garton speaking,' said the voice.

'This is Miriam Severo. I'm phoning from Rio de Janeiro,' said Miriam. 'I'm a friend of Rufus Garton.'

'Oh yes, Rufus has told us about you,' said Neil. 'Russell Bowden is here with me now.'

'I sent a package to you yesterday,' Miriam said. 'I sent it by courier.'

39

'OK. Perhaps the package will arrive here tomorrow morning,' said Neil. 'When it arrives, we'll put it in a safe place.'

'No!' said Miriam quickly. 'Don't do that. There's been a change of plan. Please send the package back to me immediately. I need the package here.'

'Why? Is there something wrong?' asked Neil.

'Yes, there is,' Miriam replied quietly. 'My father and Rufus Garton have been kidnapped.'

Neil told Russell what Miriam had said. Russell took the phone from Neil.

'What happened?' Russell asked Miriam.

'I had a phone call about an hour ago,' said Miriam. 'It was from a man. He said, "Your father wants you to come to him." I asked to speak to my father. The man said, "He is not near a phone." Then he said, "Come and bring the package with you." He was talking about the package that I posted to Neil.'

'So your father and Rufus haven't told them anything,' said Russell. 'They don't know where the package is.'

'But the kidnappers want to speak to me again, tomorrow morning,' said Miriam. 'The man told me to wait by the phone, here in my father's office.'

Neil heard Miriam's words. He shouted at the phone, 'It's a trap Miriam! If you wait beside the phone, they will know where you are. It will be easy for them to make you a prisoner too. You must go to the police.'

'I can't do that,' replied Miriam. 'The man who phoned said, "Don't go to the police. If you talk to the police, we will know about it. We will kill your father." '

Russell Bowden made a quick decision.

'You're right, Miriam,' he said. 'The police can't do anything to help you. But you need help. And help is coming. We must fight Lurcher. I am going to catch the first plane to Rio. I'll bring the notes with me. And I'll ask Neil to come with me too.'

'Of course I'll come to Rio with you!' said Neil.

'Miriam, Neil will come too,' said Russell. 'We'll phone you again tomorrow morning. We'll come to Rio as quickly as we can.'

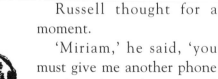

Russell thought for a moment.

'Miriam,' he said, 'you must give me another phone number. A number where I can call you tomorrow. Don't wait in your father's office. Neil is right. It's a trap. The kidnappers will know where you are. And if they know where you are, they'll be able to kidnap you!'

'You're right,' said Miriam. 'I'll ask Roberto – Father's secretary – to deal with them. He'll tell the kidnappers to phone the other number. And I'll wait at that same number for your call.'

'Where are you going to go?' asked Russell.

'Let me think for a moment,' said Miriam. 'Yes, I know. The Hotel Meridien, opposite Copacabana Beach.'

'Good!' said Russell. 'I have stayed there, so I know where it is. I'll get the phone number of the hotel from International Enquiries. You must tell the hotel reception about me. Then the receptionist will give me the telephone number of your room.'

'OK, I'll take a room there,' Miriam said. 'And I'll wait there until I hear from you,'

Miriam could not go back to her flat. She could not go to Rufus Garton's flat. She had to keep away from the kidnappers.

She went straight to the Hotel Meridien and she took a room there.

There was a private phone in Miriam's room. No one in the hotel reception would know when she made a phone call. And the kidnappers would not know where she was staying.

―――――

Early the next morning, Miriam phoned her father's office. She told Roberto what had happened.

'If anyone asks for me,' she said, 'tell them to phone me on this number – 275 9922.'

Miriam put down the phone. What could she do now? She had to keep the kidnappers waiting. That would be easy! But she had to find out where they were holding her father and Rufus Garton. How could she do that?

Miriam sat quietly and she made a plan.

6

On Top of Sugarloaf

On Wednesday morning, Neil woke up very early. He made some coffee and he woke Russell.

'I didn't sleep well, Neil,' Russell said. 'I was worried about you and this visit to Rio. It might be very dangerous!'

'Don't worry,' said Neil. 'We talked about this problem last night. You are going to pay for my air ticket. And the cost of the air ticket is the only thing that could stop me coming with you.'

'OK,' said Russell. 'Let's have some breakfast and then I'll phone the Brazilian airline – Varig.'

Half and hour later, Russell phoned the airline.

'Good morning. Varig Airline,' the booking-clerk said. 'Can I help you?'

'I want to fly to Rio de Janeiro,' Russell said.

'Good! Rio is a wonderful city!' said the booking-clerk. 'There are flights to Rio every Sunday, Wednesday and Friday.

'Today is Wednesday,' the man went on, 'so there is a flight today. It leaves London at twenty-two hundred hours – that's ten o'clock this evening. If you take that flight, you will get to Rio at eight-thirty tomorrow morning, local time.'

'Can I book two tourist-class seats on tonight's flight?' Russell asked.

The booking-clerk was silent for a few moments. Then he spoke.

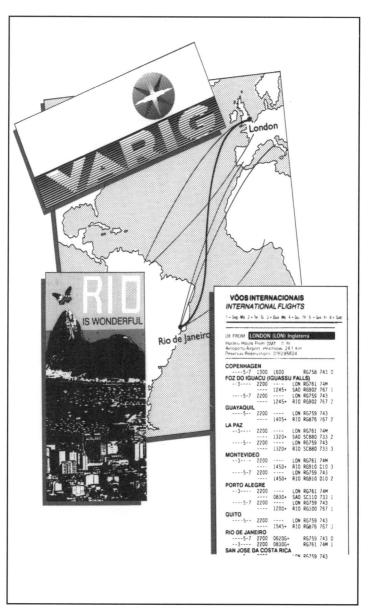

'Rio is a wonderful city!' said the booking-clerk.

'Yes,' he said. 'There are two seats available in tourist class. Can I have the names of the travellers, please?'

———

Now Neil and Russell had to move quickly. They had a lot of packing to do. But first, they had to wait for the courier. They could not leave Brighton without the package from Brazil. Would the package arrive this morning? Would it arrive in time?

At eleven o'clock, there was a knock at the door. Neil ran to open it. The courier was there, and he was holding the important package from Rio. The package had come all the way from Rio to Brighton. Now, it had to go all the way back to Rio again!

Russell phoned Miriam straight away. Miriam was waiting for his call. The phone rang and she picked it up.

'Miriam, is that you? It's Russell here,' the inventor said. 'We've got good news for you. The package has arrived. We will leave from London Airport tonight, and we will arrive in Rio tomorrow morning, at half-past eight, your time.'

'I'm very grateful,' said Miriam. 'I will feel better when you are here.'

'Don't come to the airport to meet us,' said Russell. 'We'll come to the hotel. We'll meet you there. You'll know me when you see me. I've got long white hair and I wear thick glasses.'

Neil took the phone from Russell.

'It's Neil here, Miriam,' he said. 'Have the kidnappers phoned you yet?'

'No. I'm waiting for their call now,' Miriam said. 'But

don't worry, Neil. I'll be all right. I'm going to try to trick them. I want to find out where they have taken Dad and Rufus.'

'Be careful, Miriam,' said Neil.

'I must put the phone down now,' Miriam said. 'The phone must be free when the kidnappers call me!'

'We'll see you tomorrow morning, then,' said Neil. 'I'm looking forward to meeting you. Goodbye.'

'Goodbye, Neil,' said the girl.

Miriam put the phone down. One minute later, it rang again. It was one of the kidnappers.

'I told you to wait in your father's office,' said an angry voice. 'Where are you?'

'I've been looking for the package,' said Miriam. 'I've found an envelope. Perhaps it's what you want.'

'Bring it to us,' said the rough voice. 'We're waiting for you in your father's office.'

'No,' said Miriam. 'I will not come to you. You must come to me!'

There was silence for a few moments.

'All right, I'll come to you,' said the voice. 'Where are you?'

'I'll meet you on the top of Sugarloaf,' Miriam said. 'In the Café Boa Vista. I'll wait for you here. I'll be sitting at a table near the door.'

Miriam put the phone down quickly. Then she went downstairs and bought a large envelope from the hotel shop. She wrote on it in large letters.

Miriam took a taxi to the cable-car station at the bottom of Sugarloaf. She got into the cable-car and went to the top of the mountain. It was early in the day, and there were not many people in the café.

One of the waiters was a friend of Miriam's. He was in the café that morning. He agreed to help her and she gave the envelope to him.

Some minutes later, a fat man wearing a panama hat came into the Café Boa Vista. He did not see a girl sitting at any of the tables. He spoke to the waiter.

'Has a girl been in here this morning?' he asked. 'A tall girl with long dark hair? She's about twenty-one years old.'

'Yes,' replied the waiter. 'A young woman was in here a few minutes ago. But she went out suddenly and she left an envelope lying on a table. There's a name on the envelope – Rufus Garton.'

'That's *my* name,' said the fat man quickly.

The waiter gave him the envelope. The fat man tore the envelope open. There was a message inside it.

I have not found the package. Ring me tomorrow morning on the same number.　　Miriam Severo

A moment later, the fat man ran out of the café.

7

Miriam's Plan

On Thursday morning, the flight from London arrived in Rio at 8.30 a.m. Russell and Neil took a taxi to the Hotel Meridien. Miriam was waiting for them.

As soon as Russell walked into the hotel, Miriam recognised him. Miriam and the two Englishmen had some breakfast in the hotel dining-room. Then they went up to the girl's room. Miriam told them about her adventure on the top of Sugarloaf.

'After I gave the envelope to the waiter, I stood outside the café. Then I saw a short, fat man with a panama hat go into the café. He spoke to the waiter. The waiter gave him the envelope.'

'Perhaps it was the man called Pete,' said Neil. 'I saw him in Brighton with Lurcher. He was short and fat. And he did have a panama hat.'

'I followed this man back down in the cable-car,' Miriam went on. 'He took a taxi to the marina in Gloria Bay. He got onto a yacht called the *Oil King*. There was a man on the deck of the yacht. He looked very angry when he saw the fat man alone.'

'That was Lurcher for sure,' said Neil.

'So – what happened next?' asked Russell.

'The yacht started to leave the marina,' said Miriam. 'But I was lucky. I saw a friend of mine at the marina. She has a power-boat. I asked her if I could borrow it. I took the boat and I followed the *Oil King*.'

'I took the power-boat and I followed the Oil King.'

'Did Lurcher see you?' asked Russell.

'No,' replied Miriam. 'There are hundreds of yachts and boats in the Bay. I followed the *Oil King* to a private island. There are many small private islands between Rio and Niteroi. Look!'

She spread a map out on the table.

'There is a small island here,' Miriam said. She put her finger on the map. 'The *Oil King* was in this little bay. And there is a large villa in the centre of the island. That is where the kidnappers have taken my father and Rufus. I'm sure of this!'

'Well, we must go to the police now,' said Russell. 'We must talk to them immediately.'

'Yes! But we must be careful,' said Miriam. 'The police won't believe a crazy story about electric cars. They won't believe a story about a rich man who keeps prisoners on an island. But I've thought of a plan.'

'These little islands are often used by drug smugglers,' she went on. 'I'll tell the police, "There are drugs hidden on Dr Lurcher's island." And that will be true!'

'What do you mean?' asked Neil.

'When I followed the *Oil King* to Lurcher's island, I saw another yacht there,' Miriam replied. 'My father is a lawyer and I often go to the law court with him. I've seen the owner of that other yacht in the court. He has had to answer questions in the court – questions about smuggling drugs! Perhaps he's selling drugs to Lurcher.'

'The police will listen to *that* story,' said Russell.

'But my father and Rufus must not be on the island when the police get there,' said Miriam. 'Lurcher might tell the police, "*They* are the smugglers." We must rescue Dad and Rufus from the island before the police arrive.'

'But how can we get them off the island?' asked Russell.

'Listen to my plan,' said Miriam. 'The kidnappers are going to phone me here at the Hotel Meridien today. When they phone, I'll tell them, "I've found the package. It's waiting for you at my father's office."'

'But they might not believe you,' said Russell.

'I'll read them the first page of Rufus Garton's notes,' said Miriam. 'Then they'll believe me.'

'And what do we do then?' asked Neil.

'I'll borrow my friend's power-boat again,' replied Miriam. 'I'll speak to the kidnappers on the phone. Then we'll go to Lurcher's island. Near the island, I'll get off the boat. I'll swim to the south side of the island. You must drive the power-boat into the bay on the north side of the island.'

'When you're in the bay,' Miriam went on, 'you must make a lot of noise. Lurcher will hear you and he will be angry. He'll want to know what's happening. Lurcher and his men will go down to the north shore. While they are busy with you, I'll get into the villa. I'll find my father and Rufus, and I'll free them. When you see Lurcher and his men, drive the boat quickly to the south side of the island. Rufus, Father and I will be waiting for you.'

'What about guards?' asked Neil. 'There will be guards. Perhaps they'll catch you before you find the prisoners.'

'Yes, perhaps they will catch me. It will be dangerous,' said Miriam. 'But can you think of a better plan?'

At that moment, the phone began to ring. Miriam answered it. Lurcher himself was calling, and he was angry. He was angry because Miriam was giving him a lot of trouble. And he was angry because his two prisoners would not tell him anything.

'I've found your package,' said Miriam. 'I'm going to take it to my father's office now. I'll be waiting for you there.'

'Are you trying to trick me again?' asked Lurcher angrily.

'No. I've got the notes of Mr Garton's project here,' said the girl. 'Listen!'

And she began to read the first page of Rufus Garton's notes.

'OK,' said Lurcher, after a minute. 'But listen to me. Listen carefully! If the package is not in your father's office in two hours, you'll get a present from me. You'll get it this evening. I'll send you the ring that your father wears on his left hand. And the ring will still be on his finger!'

Lurcher put down his phone. Then Miriam rang her father's office. She spoke to Roberto. Roberto was very worried.

'Don't worry,' Miriam told him. 'Everything is all right. But I need your help. A man will phone and ask if you have a package for him. Say, "Yes. It is here." But when he comes for the package, say. "It is not here any longer. Miriam has taken it away. She is waiting for you on the island." Tell him that.

'As soon as this man leaves the office,' Miriam went on, 'phone the police. Tell them, "I have some information about drug smuggling on one of the islands in the bay." Here's the map reference for the island. Write it down carefully, Roberto, and give it to the police.'

Roberto wrote down the map reference.

'When are you and your father coming back?' Roberto asked.

'Very soon,' replied Miriam. 'Very soon.'

Miriam put the phone down and turned to Russell and Neil.

'Now we must move quickly,' she said, 'or my father will lose one of his fingers!'

8

The Rescue

Russell and Neil followed Miriam down to the marina.
On the way, they bought a large radio-cassette player
and some tapes. At the marina, they got into the power-
boat and Miriam drove towards Lurcher's island. Soon,
the *Oil King* passed them, sailing towards the marina.

'Did you see the man on the deck?' Neil asked
Russell. 'It was Pete. So Lurcher and Frank are on the
island.'

'But there may be other men with Lurcher,' said
Russell. 'You must be careful, Miriam!'

Miriam stopped the power-boat near the island. Then
she got into the water.

'Goodbye, Miriam,' said Neil.

'And good luck,' said Russell.

Miriam swam quietly away from the power-boat, towards the south shore of the island. Neil drove the power-boat into the small bay on the north side of the island.

———

Ten minutes later, Miriam walked quietly up the beach towards Lurcher's villa. Soon she could hear Russell and Neil in the power-boat. They were playing loud music and laughing and shouting. They were making a lot of noise.

Miriam hurried to the villa. She saw an open door. In a few moments, she was inside the building. Then, she stood still and she listened.

She heard a noise coming from beneath her. She saw a door which led to some stairs. She went through the door and down the stairs into a cellar. There were two rooms in the cellar.

Miriam opened the door to one of the rooms. Inside, her father was sitting on a chair. His arms and legs were tied to the chair and he had a gag over his mouth.

Miriam untied the gag and the ropes. She helped her father to stand up.

'Come quickly,' she said. 'We must find Rufus and get you both out of this house.'

They found Rufus in the other room of the cellar. The three of them walked quietly up the stairs and out of the villa.

The girl and the two men ran down to the beach. Suddenly, there was shouting behind them. It was Frank. He was pointing a gun at them and shouting.

But Frank was too late. In a moment, Miriam and the two men were in the power-boat, which Neil had driven to the south side of the island.

As Neil drove the power-boat away from Lurcher's island, a police boat was racing towards the bay.

'Perhaps they will find some drugs,' said Miriam. 'Now, let me introduce everybody.'

Rufus Garton looked at Neil. And Neil looked at Rufus. Then they both started laughing.

'Are we uncle and nephew?' said Rufus. 'It's possible. But does it matter? The important thing is this – we are going to be very good friends!'

Neil turned the power-boat towards the marina in Gloria bay. Suddenly, Russell spoke to Rufus.

'I have been thinking about your project for sending electricity through the air,' he began. 'It won't work.'

And that was the start of a long argument.

Neil, Miriam and Antonio sat together and laughed quietly.

Neil turned the power-boat towards the marina.

Points for Understanding

1

1 For many years, Russell Bowden had been trying to make a new kind of battery. Why?
2 People who wanted to sell oil were Russell's enemies. Why was this?
3 Dr Lurcher was not worried about Russell's assistant, Neil Garton. But he was worried about another person called Garton. Why?

2

1 A courier brought a package for Russell. Why was there a clock in the package?
2 'Perhaps this man is my uncle,' said Neil. Why did he say this?

3

1 'My phones are bugged,' said Rufus. What did he mean?
2 Russell wanted Rufus to send his notes to the workshop. But Antonio Severo was going to send them to Neil's home. Why?

4

1 Four men were helping Dr Lurcher with his kidnap plans. What were their names? Describe the men.
2 When Frank kidnapped Rufus, he used an old trick. What was this trick?

5

1 Dr Lurcher was Rufus Garton's enemy. Can you think of a reason for this?
2 Why did Miriam want Neil to send the package back to Rio?
3 Miriam took a room at the Hotel Meridien. Why?

6

1 Miriam did not want to meet Lurcher's men on Wednesday, so she used a trick. What was this trick?
2 The flight from London to Rio is a long one. How many hours does it take?

7

1 Miriam was going to tell the police a story about drug smugglers on Lurcher's island.
   (a) Why?
   (b) Was the story true?
2 Miriam wanted to rescue Rufus and her father from the island and she had a plan. What did she want Neil and Russell to do?

8

Neil, Miriam and Antonio sat together and they laughed quietly. Why did they laugh?

Macmillan Heinemann English Language Teaching, Oxford

A division of Macmillan Publishers Limited

Companies and representatives throughout the world

ISBN 0 333 74201 X

Heinemann is a registered trademark of Reed Educational & Professional Publishing Limited

Text © John Milne 1991
Design and illustration © Macmillan Publishers Limited 1998
First published 1991 as part of the Focus Reading Series
This edition published 1998

This story is entirely fictional and is not intended to depict any real persons, companies, organisations or institutions.

Illustrated by Mark Peppé
Typography by Adrian Hodgkins
Designed by Sue Vaudin
Cover by Richard Jones and Marketplace Design
Typeset in 11.5/14.5pt Goudy
Printed and bound in Great Britain by Fine Print (Services) Ltd., Oxford

98 99 00 01 02 10 9 8 7 6 5 4 3 2 1